Level **G**

Vocabulary Links

for English Language Development

Acknowledgments

Cover *statues:* www.istockphoto.com/Cliffwass; *camel:* www.shutterstock.com, Andrey Burmakin; *space:* NASA/JPL-Caltech; Page 4: Special Collections, National Agricultural Library; Page 7: Estella Hickman; Page 14: © Copyright Eastman Kodak Company; Page 18: www.istockphoto.com/gmnicholas; Page 25: Margaret Lindmark; Page 28: Hubble Space Telescope, by Matt Malkan PI, UCLA Astronomy, obtained with the PC2 through a broad red filter; Page 32: www.shutterstock.com, Donald R. Swartz; Page 35: Dr. Ronald H. Cohn/The Gorilla Foundation/koko.org; Page 44: J. Hughes, USDA Forest Service; Page 51: courtesy of Sally V. Fox; Page 55: Library of Congress, Prints and Photographs Division, LC-USZ62-7816; Page 58: US Marine Corps photograph by Pfc. Mary Rose Xenikakis; Page 69: www.istockphoto.com; Page 72: www.shutterstock.com, Maksym Gorpenyuk

ISBN 978-0-8454-7098-5

Copyright © 2012 The Continental Press, Inc.

 Continental

D1211261

Contents

Lesson 1   **The Boll Weevil** 3

Lesson 2   **The Greenhouse Effect** 6

            Review 9

Lesson 3   **The Trail of Tears** 10

Lesson 4   **Money Machines** 13

            Review 16

Lesson 5   **The Tomb of King Tut** 17

Lesson 6   **The Respiratory and Circulatory Systems** 20

            Review 23

Lesson 7   **The Diary of Anne Frank** 24

Lesson 8   **Shedding Light on Black Holes** 27

            Review 30

Lesson 9   **The Statue of Liberty** 31

Lesson 10   **Fine Animal Person Gorilla** 34

            Review 37

Midway Review 38

Lesson 11   **Inupiat Eskimos** 40

Lesson 12   **The Day the Mountain Exploded** 43

            Review 46

Lesson 13   **The Treasures of Lascaux** 47

Lesson 14   **Colored Cotton** 50

            Review 53

Lesson 15   **Underground Conductor** 54

Lesson 16   **Fire in the Oil Fields** 57

            Review 60

Lesson 17   **Bertha von Suttner** 61

Lesson 18   **The Unfinished Zebra** 64

            Review 67

Lesson 19   **The Great Wall of China** 68

Lesson 20   **Earth and the Moon** 71

            Review 74

Posttest 75

Glossary 77

The Boll Weevil

Study each word and its meaning.

attraction (noun) something that draws people's attention
attractions
We saw many famous historical *attractions* while on vacation.

diversify (verb) to give a variety to; vary
diversifies, diversified, diversifying
We are going to *diversify* the vegetable crop in our garden this year.

economy (noun) management of money and goods
economies
The president explained that the country's *economy* was in good shape.

larva (noun) the wormlike form of a newly hatched insect
larvae
A caterpillar is the *larva* of a butterfly.

profitable (adjective) making money
Mr. Bailey runs a very *profitable* computer repair business.

ravaged (adjective) completely destroyed
It will take years for the *ravaged* coastline to return to normal.

snout (noun) the long front part of the head of an animal
snouts
The trainer tapped the dog on its *snout* to get its attention.

speculate (verb) to come up with an idea that is mostly based on theory
speculates, speculated, speculating
The detective *speculated* that the burglar was a teenager.

Read each sentence below. Complete it with a word from the box.

| economy | snout | diversifying | speculated |
| larvae | attraction | profitable | ravaged |

1 My brother _____ that his team would win the game.

2 The demolition derby was the main _____ at the fair.

3 The mayor spoke of a plan to boost the city's _____.

4 My parents talked about _____ their savings plan.

5 The band fundraiser turned out to be very _____.

6 We searched for insect _____ on our hike.

7 The rainstorms didn't help the already _____ crops.

8 The pig stuck its _____ through the wire fence.

Read this story. Then go back and circle the words in the passage that you have been studying and write them on the lines below.

Enterprise, Alabama, is the home of one of America's oddest tourist attractions. It's a statue of a woman. In her upraised hands, she holds—an insect! Her companion is a beetle with a long snout. The statue may be the world's only monument to a bug.

In nature, the boll weevil is gray and about one-quarter inch long. Its only food is the cotton plant. It lays its eggs in cotton bolls, the seed pods of the plant, from which cotton thread is made. The larvae hatch in three to five days and become adults in about three weeks. Both larvae and adults eat their way through the cotton bolls. They may breed four or five times in a growing season. In a year, they can destroy a farmer's cotton crop.

At one time, the economy of the South was built on cotton. Many farmers grew nothing but cotton. It was the surest way to make money. Even after the Civil War put an end to slavery, cotton was still the South's most profitable crop.

Then along came the boll weevil. It spread outward at a rate of about 70 miles per year. It destroyed cotton crops across the Southern states.

In 1915, the boll weevil reached Alabama. In a year, the cotton crop was ravaged. Farmers had no crop to sell, so they had no money to buy goods. Storekeepers began to close their doors. Then a local businessman speculated that cotton farmers should grow peanuts instead of cotton. He convinced one farmer to do so. The farmer grew 8,000 bushels of peanuts. The boll weevil had left him deeply in debt. But with his peanut crop, he was able to pay off what he owed and even save a little money. Other farmers saw that they didn't have to depend on cotton. They could make more money by diversifying their crops. By 1919, the farmers were doing well again.

Then another businessman thought of building a monument to the boll weevil. At first, the statue was holding a fountain over her head. It wasn't until later that a local artist added an actual boll weevil. People travel from all over to see this curious monument to the bug that almost eradicated the South—and ended up saving it.

1 _____

2 _____

3 _____

4 _____

5 _____

6 _____

7 _____

8 _____

Bonus Word

eradicate [i•RAD•i•kayt] (verb)
to get rid of completely

Find the Word

Write the word that each group of words tells about.

speculate ravaged	economy profitable	snout larva	diversify attraction	eradicate

1 making money   _____

2 to vary   _____

3 to come up with an idea that is mostly based on theory   _____

4 to get rid of completely   _____

5 something that draws people's attention   _____

6 the long front part of an animal's head   _____

7 completely destroyed   _____

8 management of money and goods   _____

9 the wormlike form of a newly hatched insect   _____

Word Work

A suffix is added to the end of a word and changes its part of speech. The suffix *ify* can change an adjective to a verb.

diverse + **ify** = **diversify** (to vary or spread around)
    adj.   v.

Think of four other words that end with the suffix *ify*. Write them on the lines below. Be ready to explain what each word means and use it in a sentence.

1 _____   **3** _____

2 _____   **4** _____

The Greenhouse Effect

Study each word and its meaning.

atmosphere (noun) the air that surrounds Earth

> Smoke is absorbed into the *atmosphere*.

barrier (noun) something that blocks movement

> *barriers*
> The orange cones were placed along the road as a *barrier*.

endanger (verb) to threaten or expose to harm

> *endangers, endangered, endangering*
> Garbage pollution has *endangered* the world's oceans.

habitat (noun) a place where a plant or animal naturally lives

> *habitats*
> The zoo just completed a new *habitat* for the bears.

pollute (verb) to make the environment dirty or impure

> *pollutes, polluted, polluting*
> Chemicals from nearby factories *polluted* the lake.

reflect (verb) to send back light rays from a surface

> *reflects, reflected, reflecting*
> Light *reflected* off the shiny new car.

retain (verb) to keep; to hold in

> *retains, retained, retaining*
> The sponge *retains* water.

species (noun) a group of similar plants or animals

> Our teacher was able to identify several *species* of birds on our field trip.

Read each sentence below. Complete it with a word from the box.

barrier	pollute	reflected	habitat
retain	endangered	atmosphere	species

1 The construction site has _____ the birds in the area.

2 Certain _____ of elephants may become extinct.

3 The coral reef created a _____ in the ocean.

4 Earth's _____ is composed of many layers of gases.

5 Mom will _____ my grandmother's ring until I am old enough to have it.

6 Exhaust from many forms of transportation _____ the environment.

7 The sun _____ off the gym equipment on the playground.

8 The tiger _____ featured a pond and lots of large rocks and trees.

Read this story. Then go back and circle the words in the passage that you have been studying and write them on the lines below.

The world is getting warmer. Some say it is because of natural changes that happen over thousands of years. A number of scientists, however, say that the earth is becoming warmer because of what people are doing. A name given to the warming of the earth is the "greenhouse effect."

The greenhouse effect is named after a greenhouse, which is a glass house in which people grow plants. A greenhouse creates indoor warmth from the rays of the sun. The sun's rays go through the glass. Some are absorbed by the plants and soil. Others are reflected back to the glass roof and sides. A few of the rays go back through the glass. However, many are trapped inside, causing the greenhouse to stay warm, even in winter.

With global warming, the entire earth may start to be like a greenhouse. Gases from smokestacks and exhaust from cars float up and pollute the atmosphere. These gases form a kind of barrier, insulating the earth by retaining more of the sun's heat. When the sun's rays strike the earth, they go through the atmosphere. Unable to reflect off the earth and go back into space, the sun's rays cannot escape. They are trapped by the polluted atmosphere, which acts like the glass in a real greenhouse. As a result, the earth grows warmer, creating water vapor.

If the world's temperature keeps rising, big changes could take place—not all of them good. Lands where it is now too cold to grow food could become warm enough to support food crops. On the other hand, the polar ice caps could melt, leading to a rise in sea level. If this happened, areas near the coast would be flooded by ocean water. This would not only destroy property, but would also endanger water supplies and natural habitats. Plant and animal species would move toward higher elevations.

There is an agreement among world leaders that air pollution has to be controlled. One place to start is with cars. Automobile manufacturers are starting to build electric cars, which are cleaner. But the best thing people can do is the easiest—walk more!

1 _____

2 _____

3 _____

4 _____

5 _____

6 _____

7 _____

8 _____

Bonus Word

insulate [IN•sə•layt] (verb)

to cover with a material that prevents heat from escaping

Find the Word

Write the word that each group of words tells about.

| atmosphere | insulate | retain | species | barrier |
| endanger | pollute | habitat | reflect | |

1 a place where a plant or animal naturally lives _____

2 to send back light rays from a surface _____

3 something that blocks movement _____

4 the air that surrounds Earth _____

5 to make the environment dirty or impure _____

6 a group of similar plants or animals _____

7 to keep _____

8 to threaten or expose to harm _____

9 to cover with a material that prevents heat from escaping _____

Word Work

Some words, such as *atmosphere,* have more than one meaning. The dictionary explains these different meanings.

atmosphere (noun) the air that surrounds Earth
atmosphere (noun) the general environment of a place

Look up the word *support* in the dictionary. Choose two meanings of the word. Write them on the lines below. Then use each word in a sentence.

support (verb) _____

_____

support (noun) _____

_____

REVIEW

Read each clue. Then solve the puzzle.

Across

1 management of money and goods
2 to send back light rays from a surface
4 the air that surrounds Earth
6 to threaten or expose to harm
9 to come up with an idea that is mostly based on theory
11 to keep
12 something that blocks movement
13 a group of similar plants or animals
15 something that draws people's attention
16 making money

Down

1 to get rid of completely
2 completely destroyed
3 a place where a plant or animal lives
5 wormlike form of an insect
7 to vary
8 to cover with material that prevents heat from escaping
10 to make the environment dirty or impure
14 a long front part of the head of an animal

The Trail of Tears

Study each word and its meaning.

cooperate (verb) to work together

cooperates, cooperated, cooperating
Everyone *cooperated* to put on the play.

expand (verb) to become larger; to grow in size

expands, expanded, expanding
The giant balloon *expanded* as the hot air filled it.

federal (adjective) relating to the central government of a country

Each year, many US citizens pay both state and *federal* taxes.

forbid (verb) to not allow; to order not to do

forbids, forbade, forbidden, forbidding
The law *forbids* smoking in public buildings.

guarantee (verb) to promise; to make certain

guarantees, guaranteed, guaranteeing
Can you *guarantee* that I will not have to replace this battery soon?

provision (noun) a part of an agreement

A *provision* of the contract allows us to sell the building.

sacred (adjective) holy

Many religions have a *sacred* book.

supreme (adjective) highest in degree

The man's donation was a *supreme* act of kindness.

Read each sentence below. Complete it with a word from the box.

expand supreme	federal cooperate	forbids sacred	guaranteed provision

1 The capital of the _____ government is in Washington, D.C.

2 A _____ in Amber's contract said she had to work at least 40 hours a week.

3 A dictator is the _____ ruler of a land.

4 Ashley did not _____ with the rest of the group.

5 They _____ that these new tires would last for 50,000 miles.

6 Most religions have a _____ place for prayer.

7 Do you think the football league will _____ to add new teams?

8 The law _____ fishing and hunting without a license.

Read this story. Then go back and circle the words in the passage that you have been studying and write them on the lines below.

For hundreds of years, the Cherokees have lived in parts of Georgia, Tennessee, and Alabama. In the late 1700s, these American Indians and their white neighbors signed a treaty. A provision of the treaty guaranteed that the land would belong to the Cherokee nation "…as long as the rivers flow and the grass grows."

When the United States began to expand, white settlers wanted the rich Cherokee farms for themselves. The fact that oil was found on Cherokee land only increased their greed. In 1832, the federal government passed a law forbidding the Cherokees to own land. It usurped their homes and farms. Then it sold the land to white settlers.

The government ordered the Cherokees to move to poor land in what is now Oklahoma. Most of the Cherokees refused to go. "This is our home," they said. "We were here long before the white man came. This land is sacred to us." Instead of fighting with weapons, they fought peacefully in the courts.

After eight long years, the Cherokees won their case in the United States Supreme Court. Yet two American presidents refused to cooperate with the decision. The Cherokees' battle was lost.

In the fall of 1838, the US Army marched into Cherokee lands. They gathered together 13,000 men, women, and children. The thousand-mile journey to their new home lasted six months. Most of the people walked, and death walked with them. Hunger, cold, and sickness killed almost 4,000 Cherokees. Graves along the route still mark this terrible "Trail of Tears."

1 _____

2 _____

3 _____

4 _____

5 _____

6 _____

7 _____

8 _____

Bonus Word

usurp [yoo•SURP] (verb)
to take by force, usually without rights

Find the Word

Write the word that each group of words tells about.

federal	cooperate	expand	sacred	forbid
provision	supreme	usurp	guarantee	

1 to promise _____

2 to not allow _____

3 a part of an agreement _____

4 holy _____

5 to work together _____

6 highest in degree _____

7 relating to the central government of a country _____

8 to become larger _____

9 to take by force _____

Word Work

Some words, such as *sign,* have more than one meaning. The dictionary explains these different meanings.

sign (noun) something that conveys information
sign (noun) a mark or symbol that stands for a word

Look up the word *court.* Choose two meanings of the word. Write them below and use them in a sentence.

court (noun) _____

_____

court (noun) _____

_____

Money Machines

Study each word and its meaning.

access (noun) permission to use something

accesses
I had to change my password to get *access* to the website.

automatic (adjective) operating by itself

The man in the wheelchair pushed a button to open the *automatic* door.

deduct (verb) to take away from an account

deducts, deducted, deducting
My payment was *deducted* from the amount I owe.

deposit (verb) to put money into an account

deposits, deposited, depositing
I *deposited* half of my babysitting money in the bank.

dispense (verb) to give out

dispenses, dispensed, dispensing
When Carter put a quarter in the machine, it *dispensed* candy.

install (verb) to put in a position for use

installs, installed, installing
The worker came to *install* the new shower door.

payment (noun) money given in exchange for goods or services

payments
My brother made his last car *payment* this month.

selective (adjective) choosy or picky

I wanted to be *selective* about who I invited to the party.

Read each sentence below. Complete it with a word from the box.

deposited	selective	automatic	dispenses
access	install	payment	deduct

1 After I write a check, I must remember to _____ the amount from my account.

2 Dad will _____ a basketball net in the driveway.

3 Sal got a notice that his _____ was late.

4 You must use a special card key to have _____ to the computer room.

5 Mom is _____ about what type of apples she uses in her pie.

6 The scout leader _____ the bake sale money on Saturday.

7 This machine _____ tokens to use at the arcade.

8 Our new refrigerator had an _____ ice dispenser.

Read this story. Then go back and circle the words in the passage that you have been studying and write them on the lines below.

For most people waiting in line seems like a waste of time. But, Don Wetzel got an idea for a valuable invention while he was waiting in line. Wetzel was standing in line at a bank in Dallas in 1968 when he imagined a machine that would deduct money from your bank account and give it to you. Wetzel worked with two other men, and within a year the team had created a model of a machine that could be placed in a bank and would dispense money to customers automatically. The first machine cost five million dollars to develop and was called an automatic teller machine, or ATM.

The first successful ATM was installed in the wall outside Chemical Bank in New York City, and it only gave out money. Later, the machines were improved to let customers deposit money, to make payments for bills, and to do most of the transactions that a bank teller does. The first ATMs were not connected by computer to a bank's accounts. So banks were selective about who could use an ATM. Only people with bank credit could use the machine. After ATMs were connected to a bank's computer system, ATM cards were developed that included individual account information. Therefore, more and more people had access to ATMs. Because they are quick, easy to use, and open all the time, ATMs have become popular. They are now found in stores as well as banks all over the world.

1 _____

2 _____

3 _____

4 _____

5 _____

6 _____

7 _____

8 _____

Bonus Word

transaction [tran•SAK•shən] (noun)
a business dealing

Find the Word

Write the word that each group of words tells about.

install	transaction	access	deposit	payment
deduct	automatic	dispense	selective	

1 money given in exchange for goods _____

2 permission to use something _____

3 to put money into an account _____

4 operating by itself _____

5 to take away from an amount _____

6 to put in a position for use _____

7 a business dealing _____

8 choosy or picky _____

9 to give out _____

Word Work

A prefix is added to the beginning of a word and changes its meaning. The prefix *auto* means "self."

automatic operating by itself

Look up each word in a dictionary. Tell how "self" is part of its meaning.

1 autopilot _____

2 autobiography _____

3 autograph _____

4 automobile _____

Read the meanings. Then find and circle each word in the puzzle.
Look across and down.

```
T  O  B  P  R  A  N  I  C  R  O  D  N  U  A  C  C  E  S  S  E
O  R  E  M  C  U  S  U  P  R  E  M  E  S  P  N  T  V  U  T  X
P  Y  F  E  H  T  U  I  R  O  V  E  N  G  O  O  P  E  C  E  A
S  D  P  A  O  O  P  V  A  I  P  N  D  U  Y  M  I  R  C  P  L
Y  T  S  P  I  M  R  O  D  M  V  I  S  A  E  X  P  A  N  D  F
T  R  A  N  S  A  C  T  I  O  N  B  E  R  D  E  C  P  C  E  E
A  C  C  E  S  T  U  M  S  C  T  B  L  A  E  F  O  R  B  I  D
D  E  R  D  E  I  U  C  P  A  Y  M  E  N  T  T  O  O  I  L  E
E  D  E  D  U  C  T  C  E  P  L  S  C  T  W  V  P  V  K  Y  R
P  E  D  E  R  P  I  C  N  N  S  R  T  E  A  K  E  I  L  G  A
O  I  O  N  E  C  F  U  S  U  R  P  I  E  M  V  R  S  P  I  L
S  N  G  A  L  W  R  S  E  P  M  A  V  L  W  T  A  I  S  O  T
I  N  S  T  A  L  L  K  Y  N  I  V  E  E  N  I  T  O  I  O  N
T  P  M  I  E  T  B  U  I  S  G  I  B  R  I  S  E  N  P  E  R
```

Across

- permission to use something
- highest in degree
- to grow in size
- a business dealing
- to order not to do
- money given in exchange for goods
- to take away from an amount
- to take by force
- to put in a position to use

Down

- to put money into an account
- holy
- operating by itself
- to give out
- choosy or picky
- to make certain
- to work together
- a part of an agreement
- relating to the central government of a country

The Tomb of King Tut

Study each word and its meaning.

archaeologist (noun) a person who studies how people lived in the past

archaeologists
Have *archaeologists* been able to read the strange writing on the rock?

chariot (noun) a two-wheeled cart pulled by horses

chariots
The emperor arrived by *chariot*.

entertain (verb) to hold the attention of; to amuse

entertains, entertained, entertaining
The choral group *entertained* the people at the luncheon.

jewelry (noun) objects, such as rings and necklaces, worn on the body

That piece of *jewelry* is made of silver.

mummy (noun) a body that has been preserved after death

mummies
In this scary book, an Egyptian *mummy* comes back to life.

pharaoh (noun) the title of a ruler of ancient Egypt

pharaohs
Ramesses II, a great *pharaoh* of Egypt, built huge temples.

spectacular (adjective) unusual and impressive

The Rose Bowl parade has *spectacular* floats made of flowers.

tomb (noun) a place to hold a dead body

tombs
In the old cemetery, we saw the *tombs* of several famous people.

Read each sentence below. Complete it with a word from the box.

pharaoh	**entertained**	**spectacular**	**archaeologists**
jewelry	**tomb**	**chariots**	**mummy**

1 In the movie, the _____ raced around a stadium.

2 Divers brought up a chest filled with old coins and _____.

3 The _____ studied the remains of a prehistoric village.

4 The _____ of the Unknown Soldier honors those who died for their country.

5 A magician _____ the kids at the birthday party.

6 The painting showed a _____ wearing a tall red and white crown.

7 At the museum, our class saw a _____ wrapped in strips of white cloth.

8 From the cliff, we had a _____ view of waves crashing against the rocks.

Read this story. Then go back and circle the words in the passage that you have been studying and write them on the lines below.

Howard Carter was almost afraid to look through the small hole in the door. For years he and Lord Carnarvon had been looking for the tomb of Tutankhamen. This pharaoh of ancient Egypt had become king at age 9. He had died suddenly at age 18. Would this excavation lead to the right tomb at last? Or would it be empty like all the others?

With shaking hands, Carter raised a lighted candle. He peered through the hole. "Can you see anything?" Lord Carnarvon asked impatiently. At the sight of gold glistening everywhere, Carter gasped. "Yes, wonderful things," he answered. Magnificent treasures filled the small room.

Later Carter entered the chamber of the king. There he found a coffin made of gold. Inside was the mummy of Tutankhamen. A golden mask lay upon his face, and dazzling jewelry covered his body.

Egyptians believed that life went on after death. Other rooms in the tomb held belongings that Tutankhamen would need in the next world. Statues of servants stood ready to serve him. There were chariots and boats for his travels. There were weapons for fighting. Even games had been placed there so he could entertain himself.

Before this, archaeologists had found other royal burial places in the Valley of the Kings. Almost all of them had been stripped by robbers. Only the tomb of Tutankhamen still had its riches. Yet this boy-king was not an important pharaoh. We can only imagine what spectacular treasure might have been placed in the tomb of a great one.

1 _____

2 _____

3 _____

4 _____

5 _____

6 _____

7 _____

8 _____

Bonus Word

excavation [eks•kə•VAY•shən] (noun)
the act of digging something out

Find the Word

Write the word that each group of words tells about.

chariot	mummy	entertain	archaeologist	spectacular
excavation	tomb	pharaoh	jewelry	

1   to hold the attention of   _____

2   a place to hold a dead body   _____

3   unusual and impressive   _____

4   objects worn on the body   _____

5   the act of digging something out   _____

6   a person who studies how people lived in the past   _____

7   a body that has been preserved after death   _____

8   the title of a ruler of ancient Egypt   _____

9   a two-wheeled cart pulled by horses   _____

Word Work

A prefix is added to the beginning of a word and changes its meaning. The prefix *im* means "not."

im + patiently = impatiently (not patiently)

Add the prefix *im* to each word below. Write the new word on the line and in the phrase.

1   im + pure =   _____   the _____ water

2   im + movable = _____   an _____ rock

3   im + polite =   _____   the _____ person

4   im + possible = _____   an _____ puzzle

The Respiratory and Circulatory Systems

Study each word and its meaning.

artery (noun) part of the body that carries blood away from the heart

> *arteries*
> The surgeon was careful to not cut an *artery*.

component (noun) a part of something, an ingredient

> *components*
> We did not have all the *components* to fix the television.

contract (verb) to draw all the parts together

> *contracts, contracted, contracting*
> Rob *contracted* his muscles.

digest (verb) to change food so it can be used by the body

> *digests, digested, digesting*
> I felt very full until my stomach *digested* the big meal.

expel (verb) to force out or discharge

> *expels, expelled, expelling*
> Tara's voice teacher taught her to *expel* all the air from her lungs.

function (noun) the specific purpose for something

> *functions*
> The brakes' *function* is to stop the car.

inflate (verb) to fill with air

> *inflates, inflated, inflating*
> Can you *inflate* my bike's tire?

inhale (verb) to breathe in

> *inhales, inhaled, inhaling*
> I try not to *inhale* secondhand smoke.

Read each sentence below. Complete it with a word from the box.

inflated	**expel**	**digest**	**contracted**
arteries	**inhaled**	**function**	**components**

1 In health class, we studied how veins and _____ move blood.

2 What is the _____ of this machine?

3 The clown _____ a balloon for each child.

4 Gather all the _____ for your science project.

5 It is good to let your food _____ before doing demanding exercises.

6 I slowly _____ the crisp country air.

7 The dog's muscles _____ as it ran.

8 I coughed to _____ the water from my lungs.

Read this story. Then go back and circle the words in the passage that you have been studying and write them on the lines below.

Your body gets energy from the food you eat. As cells break down the food, they produce carbon dioxide as waste. Your body needs to be able to bring oxygen to all your cells and to carry carbon dioxide away. Your respiratory and circulatory systems work together to carry out this function.

The main function of the respiratory system is to bring oxygen into your body and to remove carbon dioxide. As you inhale, your diaphragm contracts and air rushes in to inflate your lungs. First, the air moves through your nose and mouth and then eventually into your lungs. Oxygen flows into the saclike alveoli of the lungs, where it is exchanged for carbon dioxide. With your next exhale, you expel carbon dioxide.

The circulatory system works with other organ systems to help the body function. The main functions of the circulatory system are to move oxygen to cells and to move carbon dioxide away from cells, and to carry nutrients from food that has been digested to all the cells in the body. Some of the components of this system are blood, the heart, capillaries, arteries, and veins. Your heart pumps blood throughout your body to carry the materials your body needs. Capillaries surround your lungs. They move oxygen and carbon dioxide between the circulatory and respiratory systems. Arteries carry blood away from the heart. Then veins carry the blood back to the heart.

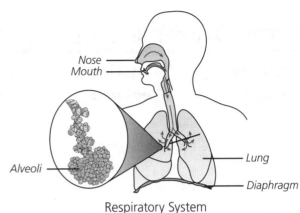

Nose
Mouth
Alveoli
Lung
Diaphragm

Respiratory System

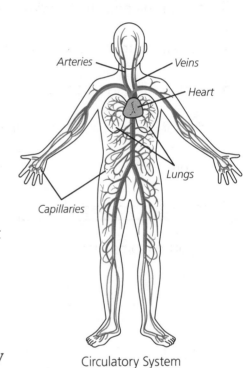

Arteries
Veins
Heart
Lungs
Capillaries

Circulatory System

Your respiratory and circulatory systems work hard to keep your body working properly. Each part of the systems is useless without the other parts.

1 _____

2 _____

3 _____

4 _____

5 _____

6 _____

7 _____

8 _____

Bonus Word

nutrient [NOO•tree•uhnt] (noun)

something that helps supply what is needed for life and health

Find the Word

Write the word that each group of words tells about.

inhale	function	component	expel	nutrient
digest	contract	inflate	artery	

1 to change food so it can be used by the body _____

2 to fill with air _____

3 part of the body that carries blood away from the heart _____

4 something that helps supply what is needed for life _____

5 to draw all parts together _____

6 the specific purpose of something _____

7 to breathe in _____

8 to force out or discharge _____

9 a part of something _____

Word Work

A suffix is added to the end of a word and changes its meaning. The suffix *less* means "without."

use + less = useless (without use)

Think of four words that end with the suffix *less*. Write them on the lines below. Be ready to explain what each word means and to use it in a sentence.

1 _____ 3 _____

2 _____ 4 _____

REVIEW

Read each meaning. Write the word in the blanks. Read the words down the boxes.
They tell you the name of the group of pharaohs to which King Tut belonged.

1
2
3
4
5
6
7
8
9
10
11
12
13
14
15
16
17

Definitions

1 part of the body that carries blood away from the heart
2 the act of digging something out
3 a person who studies how people lived in the past
4 to breathe in
5 something that helps supply what is needed for life
6 to force out or discharge
7 to amuse
8 to draw all the parts together
9 to fill with air
10 a two-wheeled cart pulled by horses
11 to change food so it can be used by the body
12 objects worn on the body
13 the specific purpose of something
14 a title of a ruler of ancient Egypt
15 unusual and impressive
16 a place to hold a dead body
17 a body that has been preserved after death

The Diary of Anne Frank

Study each word and its meaning.

betray (verb) to hand over to an enemy; to not be loyal to

> *betrays, betrayed, betraying*
> Why did the American general Benedict Arnold *betray* his country?

cruelty (noun) unkind, painful words or actions

> *cruelties*
> *Cruelty* to animals is against the law.

diary (noun) a daily record of a person's acts and thoughts

> *diaries*
> Each day I write something in my *diary*.

hatred (noun) a very strong dislike

> *Hatred* can lead people to do terrible things.

memory (noun) honor and respect for someone in the past

> *memories*
> We hung a yellow ribbon on the tree in *memory* of the prisoners of war.

occupy (verb) to take over and control something

> *occupies, occupied, occupying*
> On the bus, we should not *occupy* seats set aside for disabled people.

publish (verb) to print and offer for sale

> *publishes, published, publishing*
> Mark Twain's *The Adventures of Tom Sawyer* was *published* in 1876.

recover (verb) to get back again

> *recovers, recovered, recovering*
> The police *recovered* the stolen jewelry.

Read each sentence below. Complete it with a word from the box.

publish	hatred	betrayed	recover
cruelty	diary	occupied	memory

1 Many slaves ran away to escape the _____ of their owners.

2 After the hurricane, the National Guard _____ and protected the area.

3 The spy _____ the country by giving away important secrets.

4 American colonists showed their _____ of unjust taxes by dumping tea in Boston harbor.

5 I hope your company will soon _____ a new book by my favorite author.

6 Were you able to _____ the document from your computer?

7 Elena kept a _____ of her adventures at summer camp.

8 A tree was planted in _____ of the young accident victim.

Read this story. Then go back and circle the words in the passage that you have been studying and write them on the lines below.

It was a cold, gray day in the Dutch city of Amsterdam. Anne Frank looked out of a small window. The 14-year-old girl could see a canal and a bridge. Standing guard on the bridge was a German soldier. The world was at war. Since 1940, German troops had occupied Holland.

Throughout Europe, Jews were living in fear. Thousands of Jews had been rounded up by the German secret police and shipped to death camps. Many others had gone into hiding to escape the holocaust. Anne, her parents, and her sister had moved to secret rooms behind her father's offices.

Anne turned away from the window and sat down at a table. She opened her diary. Each day she wrote about her life and about the wonders of growing up. She also looked forward to a world free from war and fear.

One day in August 1944, Anne heard a pounding on the door. It was the German secret police. Anne's heart stood still. After 25 months, someone had betrayed her family. They were arrested and sent by train to Germany. Only Mr. Frank survived the cruelty of the death camps.

At the end of the war, Anne's father recovered his daughter's diary and had it published. *The Diary of Anne Frank* became a best-selling book, a play, and a movie. Anne Frank's life was cut short by hatred. But her words of hope have kept the memory of this remarkable young girl alive.

1 _____

2 _____

3 _____

4 _____

5 _____

6 _____

7 _____

8 _____

Bonus Word

holocaust [HOL•ə•kost] (noun)
total destruction and great loss of life

Find the Word

Write the word that each group of words tells about.

memory occupy	hatred cruelty	holocaust betray	diary publish	recover

1 to get back again   _____

2 unkind, painful words or actions   _____

3 total destruction and great loss of life   _____

4 to print and offer for sale   _____

5 a very strong dislike   _____

6 to hand over to an enemy   _____

7 honor and respect for someone in the past   _____

8 a daily record of a person's thoughts   _____

9 to take over and control something   _____

Word Work

A suffix is added to the end of a word and changes its meaning. The suffix *able* means "able to be" or "worthy of."

memory + able = memorable (worthy of remembering)

Look up each word below in a dictionary. Tell how *able* is part of its meaning.

1 breakable _____

2 perishable _____

3 laughable _____

4 believable _____

Shedding Light on Black Holes

Study each word and its meaning.

astronomer (noun) a person who studies objects in space

astronomers
The *astronomer* used a very strong telescope.

collapse (verb) to cave in; to fall apart

collapses, collapsed, collapsing
The bridge *collapsed* during the storm.

extreme (adjective) very great in measure

I felt *extreme* happiness when I won the race.

internal (adjective) located inside or within; inner

These x-rays show that you have *internal* injuries.

penetrate (verb) to see or pass through

penetrates, penetrated, penetrating
The light did not *penetrate* the heavy fog.

probable (adjective) most likely

It is *probable* that Aunt June will arrive by noon.

typically (adverb) usually, most often

We *typically* eat dinner at 6:00.

velocity (noun) speed

The train was moving at a great *velocity*.

Read each sentence below. Complete it with a word from the box.

probable	**internal**	**velocity**	**typically**
astronomer	**penetrate**	**extreme**	**collapsed**

1 My family _____ goes to the beach every summer.

2 The _____ discovered a comet.

3 My eyes could not _____ the darkness of the basement.

4 My brother took the microwave apart to see how the _____ pieces went together.

5 There was _____ excitement over the news that Grandma was coming to visit.

6 Hector used special equipment to measure the _____ of the racecar.

7 The roof of the abandoned house _____ because of strong winds.

8 It is _____ that school will be cancelled because of the snow.

Read this story. Then go back and circle the words in the passage that you have been studying and write them on the lines below.

Black holes are regions in space where gravity is so strong that not even light can escape. They are impossible to see because they trap the light necessary to see them. However, astronomers think they can detect black holes by scrutinizing other clues.

Black holes can be hard to understand. Escape velocity is the speed at which something can break free of the pull of gravity. The escape velocity of any object depends on how massive and how dense it is. Imagine an object so heavy and compressed into such a tiny volume that its escape velocity is greater than the speed of light. Because light would never by able to escape it, you could call such an object a black hole.

Black holes are typically the remains of dead stars. During the lifetime of a star, it maintains its shape because the force of the reactions inside it exactly balances the gravity holding it together. When a typical star uses up all its internal fuel, it explodes. The outer part blasts into space. The inner part collapses under its own weight. It becomes a black hole.

Scientist uses powerful instruments to penetrate deep into space. They look for stars and clouds of gas and dust that are orbiting powerful, invisible sources of gravity. As matter is pulled toward the gravity source, it heats up to extreme temperatures. This heat causes the source to give off x-rays that scientists can detect. Using this method, scientists think they have identified several probable black holes.

1 _____

2 _____

3 _____

4 _____

5 _____

6 _____

7 _____

8 _____

Bonus Word

scrutinize [SKROOT•n•ahyz] (verb)
to look at carefully

Find the Word

Write the word that each group of words tells about.

internal	collapse	probable	typically	scrutinize
astronomer	extreme	penetrate	velocity	

1 most likely   _____

2 to look at carefully   _____

3 a person who studies objects in space   _____

4 located inside or within   _____

5 to cave in   _____

6 usually   _____

7 speed   _____

8 to see or pass through   _____

9 very great in measure   _____

Word Work

Homophones are words that sound alike but are spelled differently. They also have different meanings.

pair (two of a kind)   **pare** (to peel)   **pear** (a fruit)

Look up these pairs of homophones in the dictionary. Write their meanings on the lines below and be ready to use them in a sentence.

night _____

knight _____

soar _____

sore _____

break _____

brake _____

REVIEW

Read each clue. Then solve the puzzle.

Across

6 a person who studies objects in space
9 very great in measure
11 total destruction and loss of life
12 usually, most often
14 speed
15 to cave in
17 to not be loyal to
18 a daily record of one's thoughts

Down

1 to see or pass through
2 very strong dislike
3 unkind words or actions
4 honor and respect for someone in the past
5 to look at carefully
7 located inside or within
8 to take over and control something
10 to get back again
13 most likely
16 to print and offer for sale

The Statue of Liberty

Study each word and its meaning.

alliance (noun) an agreement between two or more countries

alliances
Many countries joined the *alliance* for peace.

assemble (verb) to put together

assembles, assembled, assembling
How long will it take you to *assemble* this model car?

bestow (verb) to present as a gift

bestows, bestowed, bestowing
The mayor *bestowed* a good citizen award on my neighbor.

centennial (noun) a 100th anniversary

The bank marked its *centennial* with a weeklong celebration.

massive (adjective) very large and heavy

A *massive* mudslide came crashing down the hillside.

sculptor (noun) a person who shapes clay or carves in wood, stone, or some other material

sculptors
We watched a *sculptor* carve a swan out of a block of ice.

tyranny (noun) the cruel use of power

tyrannies
The American colonies fought a war to free themselves from the *tyranny* of the king of England.

unveil (verb) to disclose or bring into view

unveils, unveiled, unveiling
The company *unveiled* the new design of its website.

Read each sentence below. Complete it with a word from the box.

massive	assemble	alliance	tyranny
centennial	bestow	sculptor	unveil

1 Who was the _____ that carved the four presidents at Mt. Rushmore?

2 April 2012 was the _____ of the sinking of the RMS *Titanic*.

3 The artist will _____ her new painting at a showing on Friday.

4 The United States and Great Britain had an _____ during World War II.

5 The academy will _____ an achievement award on the famous actor.

6 Now that you have taken this bike apart, can you _____ it again?

7 The ship hit a _____ iceberg and sank.

8 Many people in our world live under the _____ of cruel rulers.

Read this story. Then go back and circle the words in the passage that you have been studying and write them on the lines below.

The finest gift that the United States ever received may have been the Statue of Liberty. It was bestowed on us on July 4, 1884, by the people of France. The French wanted to celebrate the friendship and alliances between the two countries.

In 1874, the French sculptor Frederic Bartholdi was given the job of designing and building the statue. First, thin sheets of copper were hammered into shape. Then a giant iron framework was constructed to support the copper plates. After nearly nine years, the workers finished the massive statue. Liberty stood 151 feet high and weighed 225 tons.

In 1884, the statue was taken apart. Each part was given a number and shipped to New York. It took almost two years to assemble the 300 pieces again. The statue was placed on Bedloe's Island in New York City.

President Grover Cleveland unveiled the statue in 1886. Since then, millions of tourists have visited it. In her right hand, Liberty holds high the torch of freedom. The tablet in her left hand reads July 4, 1776. A broken chain around the statue's feet stands for liberty breaking the chains of tyranny. On October 28, 1986, the Statue of Liberty celebrated her centennial. Even today, the Statue is a proud personification of hope and freedom for all people.

1 _____

2 _____

3 _____

4 _____

5 _____

6 _____

7 _____

8 _____

Bonus Word

personification [per•son•uh•fi•KAY•shuhn] (noun)

the representation of an idea or thing as a person

Find the Word

Write the word that each group of words tells about.

bestow	centennial	unveil	massive	personification
tyranny	alliance	assemble	sculptor	

1   the representation of an idea as a person   _____

2   very large and heavy   _____

3   a 100th anniversary   _____

4   the cruel use of power   _____

5   to put together   _____

6   to disclose or put into view   _____

7   a person who shapes or carves materials   _____

8   to present as a gift   _____

9   agreement between two or more countries   _____

Word Work

Synonyms are words that have the same, or almost the same, meaning.

massive • huge   **liberty • freedom**

Find a synonym for each of the following words. Use a dictionary or thesaurus for help. Write the synonyms on the lines below. Be ready to use them in a sentence.

1   assemble   _____   4   ancient   _____

2   genuine   _____   5   fascinating _____

3   sorrow   _____   6   site   _____

Fine Animal Person Gorilla

Study each word and its meaning.

accomplish (verb) to carry out; to complete

accomplishes, accomplished, accomplishing
We *accomplished* many things at the meeting today.

communicate (verb) to pass information so that it is received and understood

communicates, communicated, communicating
People once used smoke signals to *communicate* with one another.

confident (adjective) very sure; certain

Are you *confident* that you made the track team?

esteem (noun) good opinion; great respect

I hold my grandfather in high *esteem*.

gesture (noun) a motion of the hands, arms, or body while speaking or in place of speech

gestures
The conductor made a *gesture* to stop the music.

gorilla (noun) a large African ape with a heavy body and dark hair

gorillas
Our library has several interesting books about *gorillas*.

occasionally (adverb) happening only from time to time

Occasionally, I get a letter from my pen pal in Hawaii.

repetition (noun) saying or doing something again and again

We learned the plays for the game through *repetition*.

Read each sentence below. Complete it with a word from the box.

gorillas confident	accomplish gesture	esteem communicate	repetition occasionally

1 I have great _____ for people who have overcome tragedies.

2 Our teacher _____ takes us on interesting field trips.

3 The man made a _____ for us to cross the street.

4 Dian Fossey lived among _____ in Africa and wrote a book about them.

5 Xun memorized the poem using _____.

6 The mayor is _____ that he can settle the strike peacefully.

7 Rena uses the computer to _____ with her friends.

8 Did you _____ all the tasks on your list?

Read this story. Then go back and circle the words in the passage that you have been studying and write them on the lines below.

Koko is like many people. She occasionally tells jokes and teases. She likes to paint and play with her kitten. However, this "person" is a gorilla.

Koko does not speak aloud as many people do. She uses American Sign Language, the language of many deaf people. Words are formed by using hand gestures.

When Koko was one year old, the young gorilla lived at the San Francisco Zoo. Penny Patterson, a college student, wanted to teach Koko to communicate. She worked very hard to accomplish her goal.

Koko paints a picture she calls "Hawaii" and makes the sign for "red," the color she is using.

First, Penny began by showing Koko a bottle. Over and over she would say, "Drink." At the same time she would hold Koko's hand and form the sign for drink with her fingers. At first, Koko was more interested in getting the bottle. She did not want to be slowed down by making a sign. However, Penny did not abandon her experiment. She decided to try the word "food." After a week of repetition, Koko made the sign for food all by herself. Soon Koko could form other words.

Later, Koko moved into a special home of her own, near where Penny lived. A younger gorilla named Michael came to live with Koko and kept her company. Each day Penny taught the gorillas new words. People often ask Penny whether Koko understands what Penny is saying. Penny is confident that she does because they are able to converse. Penny tells about the phrases the animals made up on their own. Koko signed "finger bracelet" to mean ring; Michael called peas "bean balls."

Koko, especially, seems to have great esteem for herself. Once a visitor asked her whether she was a person or a gorilla. "Fine animal person gorilla," Koko replied.

1 _____

2 _____

3 _____

4 _____

5 _____

6 _____

7 _____

8 _____

Bonus Word

converse [kuhn•VURS] (verb)
to talk with someone

Find the Word

Write the word that each group of words tells about.

occasionally accomplish	esteem gorilla	confident repetition	gesture converse	communicate

1 to talk with someone _____

2 doing something again and again _____

3 a motion of the hands in place of speech _____

4 very sure; certain _____

5 to carry out _____

6 a large African ape _____

7 happening from time to time _____

8 to pass information so that it is received and understood _____

9 good opinion _____

Word Work

A suffix is added to the end of a word and changes its meaning. The suffix *or* means "one who."

visit + or = visitor (one who visits)

Add the suffix *or* to each word below. Write the new word on the line and in the phrase.

1 sail + or = _____ a brave _____

2 act + or = _____ a talented _____

3 conduct + or = _____ a well-known _____

4 invent + or = _____ a brilliant _____

REVIEW

Read the meanings. Then find and circle each word in the puzzle.
Look across and down.

```
C  N  I  R  S  E  O  R  E  P  E  T  I  T  I  O  N  T  Y  C  E  P
A  V  I  T  N  O  F  Y  N  U  K  D  I  M  D  G  U  J  U  A  C  X
C  C  O  M  M  U  N  I  C  A  T  E  O  E  N  R  I  A  L  L  D  C
C  O  S  S  T  A  M  D  E  W  N  O  C  V  E  V  A  P  S  L  M  R
O  N  B  D  U  S  L  I  P  E  V  Y  C  E  N  T  E  N  N  I  A  L
M  F  N  U  O  S  B  E  S  T  O  W  A  S  C  U  L  I  O  A  R  S
P  I  S  N  N  E  I  O  V  T  J  Y  S  B  I  T  D  J  U  N  R  S
L  D  N  V  T  M  I  C  I  G  O  R  I  L  L  A  S  E  C  C  N  C
I  E  R  E  M  B  L  G  F  N  K  I  O  M  A  M  L  O  H  E  N  U
S  N  E  I  A  L  F  E  I  L  N  E  N  S  P  A  A  O  M  F  G  L
H  T  R  L  S  E  E  S  M  K  V  Y  A  S  E  S  M  V  E  R  O  P
A  R  I  E  N  P  W  T  P  M  S  E  L  V  E  S  T  E  E  M  O  T
E  E  E  M  U  A  D  U  O  L  I  R  L  Y  P  I  T  L  E  M  T  O
A  L  C  O  N  V  E  R  S  E  N  A  Y  E  U  V  R  N  V  E  S  R
O  Y  B  I  W  E  M  E  T  Y  R  A  N  N  Y  E  P  L  M  I  Y  B
R  E  P  E  R  S  O  N  I  F  I  C  A  T  I  O  N  K  Y  N  R  E
```

Across

- saying or doing something again and again
- to pass information so that it is received and understood
- a 100th anniversary
- to present as a gift
- a large African ape
- a good opinion
- to talk with someone
- the cruel use of power
- the representation of an idea as a person

Down

- to complete
- very sure; certain
- to bring into view
- to put together
- a motion of the hands in place of speech
- happening only from time to time
- very large and heavy
- an agreement between two countries
- a person who shapes clay or carves other material

Circle the correct answer.

1 Dense is to thick as **esteem** is to _____.

A debt

B credit

C respect

D communicate

2 Record is to music as **publish** is to _____.

A writing

B editing

C surfing

D typing

3 Clothing is to shirt as **habitat** is to _____.

A forest

B statue

C house

D liberty

4 Wide is to narrow as **forbid** is to _____.

A attract

B allow

C reflect

D thick

5 Inform is to newscaster as **entertain** is to _____.

A teacher

B musician

C doctor

D carpenter

6 What is something that could be **polluted?**

A economy

B education

C environment

D electronics

7 Where would you most likely **deposit** something?

A the bank

B the supermarket

C the garage

D the hospital

8 Which of these has a **snout?**

A pig   C larva

B puppet   D mummy

9 When would you most likely use a **gesture?**

A to answer the phone

B to hail a cab

C to write an email

D to change the TV channel

10 What is something with which a **sculptor** might work?

A water

B book

C camera

D clay

MIDWAY REVIEW

Complete each sentence with a word from the box.

endangered	recover	assembling	installed	profitable	dispenses
occasionally	unveiled	guarantees	massive	occupy	
speculated	access	spectacular	confident	inhaled	

1   I am _____ that I passed the math test.

2   It took ten people to control the _____ balloons in the parade.

3   The man _____ a new water heater at our house.

4   We needed _____ to the conference room on Tuesday.

5   The zoo _____ its new ape habitat.

6   The fireworks display over the water was _____.

7   I walked in the house and _____ the aroma of freshly baked cookies.

8   The small coffee shop turned out to be very _____.

9   Carmen and her sister get together _____ for lunch.

10   Dad spent the weekend _____ the swing set for my little brother.

11   The tremors from the volcano _____ nearby villages.

12   The grocery store _____ that its prices are the lowest.

13   Mr. Torres _____ that the plan would not work.

14   The change machine only _____ quarters.

15   The reading teacher will _____ the empty classroom until December.

16   The firefighters were not able to _____ anything after the fire was out.

Inupiat Eskimos

Study each word and its meaning.

antler (noun) a bony growth on the head of an animal, such as a deer

antlers
The antelope rubbed its *antlers* on the large tree.

blubber (noun) a thick layer of fat under the skin of sea animals

Whales have layers of *blubber* to keep them warm in cold oceans.

caribou (noun) deer that live in arctic areas

The popular name for *caribou* is "reindeer."

culture (noun) the customs or way of living of a people

cultures
In some *cultures,* animals are treated with great respect.

grueling (adjective) tiring; exhausting

The last five miles of the race were *grueling.*

resource (noun) something that is a source of wealth

resources
Oil is one *resource* for our country.

technology (noun) the use of scientific knowledge in an industry

technologies
Our society uses a lot of wireless *technology.*

traditional (adjective) passed down from one generation to the next

We go to my aunt's house for a *traditional* Thanksgiving dinner.

Read each sentence below. Complete it with a word from the box.

caribou	antlers	traditional	technology
grueling	cultures	blubber	resource

1 The park rangers lead a _____ 50-mile hike every spring.

2 Ian wore a _____ Scottish kilt to the ceremony.

3 The festival celebrated many different _____.

4 The river provides a natural _____ for the nearby towns.

5 We saw several herds of _____ when we visited Alaska.

6 The local college offers classes in computer _____.

7 Long ago, oil from whale _____ was used in lamps.

8 The stag shed his _____ near the lake.

Read this story. Then go back and circle the words in the passage that you have been studying and write them on the lines below.

Inupiat Eskimos have subsisted in the Barrow area, the most northern part of Alaska, for almost 4,000 years. Life was grueling for the Inupiat. The temperature can drop to 56°F below zero during the winter months. The average summer temperature is only 40°F. Between mid-November and late January, the area is in total darkness. Between mid-May and August, the sun never sets. Knowledge of the frozen environment and how to use its resources, plus patience, were important skills to the Inupiat. Their traditional homes were along the coastal areas and hunted and fished to survive.

Spring marked the beginning of the whaling season for the Inupiat. In April and May, crews camped on the edges of the frozen sea to hunt migrating whales. Whale blubber provided food, fuel, shelter, and clothes for many villages. After the ice broke in June and July, the Inupiat turned to hunting walrus and seal. Sometimes, the Inupiat stood by a seal's breathing hole for hours and waited for it to come up for air before capturing it. During the summer, the hunting crews often traveled in sealskin-covered boats, carrying 10–12 people, to hunt herds of walrus. Fishing was also important during the summer and early fall when the ice thawed. Caribou were hunted all year long. The meat provided food, the antlers were made into tools, and the skins were used for clothing.

Although most of the Inupiat's way of life has been changed by modern technology, hunting—especially whale hunting—has stayed part of their culture.

1 _____

2 _____

3 _____

4 _____

5 _____

6 _____

7 _____

8 _____

Bonus Word

subsist [səb•SIST] (verb)

to exist

Find the Word

Write the word that each group of words tells about.

resource antler	blubber subsist	technology caribou	grueling culture	traditional

1 deer in the arctic areas   _____

2 the use of scientific knowledge in an industry   _____

3 to exist   _____

4 a thick layer of fat under the skin of sea animals   _____

5 something that is a source of wealth   _____

6 exhausting   _____

7 a bony growth on the head of a deer or other animal   _____

8 the customs of a group of people   _____

9 passed from one generation to the next   _____

Word  Work

Synonyms are words that have the same, or almost the same, meaning.

thaw • melt   **begin • start**

Find a synonym for each of the following words. Check a dictionary or thesaurus for help. Write the synonyms on the lines below. Be ready to use them in a sentence.

1 capture   _____   **4** hazardous   _____

2 always   _____   **5** disguise   _____

3 patient   _____   **6** admit   _____

The Day the Mountain Exploded

Study each word and its meaning.

barren (adjective) bare; without life
The moon is a *barren* place.

catastrophe (noun) a sudden and widespread disaster
catastrophes
The earthquake was a *catastrophe* that affected thousands of people.

crater (noun) a hollow area shaped like a bowl
craters
The rain pelted the sand and left *craters* along the beach.

dome (noun) a rounded top or roof like a half sphere
domes
The football team plays in an arena with a *dome*.

instantaneous (adjective) happening immediately
The results of the electronic test were *instantaneous*.

landscape (noun) land that is viewed as scenery
landscapes
Trees and wildflowers dotted the *landscape*.

spew (verb) to gush or send out with force
spews, spewed, spewing
The flames *spewed* out of the house's windows.

summit (noun) the highest point; top
summits
Thick clouds covered the *summit* of the mountain.

Read each sentence below. Complete it with a word from the box.

instantaneous	landscape	spewed	dome
catastrophe	summit	barren	crater

1 The computer search yielded _____ results.

2 Few plants grow in this _____ part of our country.

3 The climbers planted a flag on the _____ of the highest peak.

4 Workers repaired the _____ on the capitol building.

5 Mean words _____ out of the man's mouth.

6 The sinkhole left a large _____ in our backyard.

7 Our town received a grant to improve the _____ along Main Street.

8 The flood was a _____ that many people still talk about.

Read this story. Then go back and circle the words in the passage that you have been studying and write them on the lines below.

May 18, 1980, was a bright, clear day in the state of Washington. Mountain climbers near the summit of Mount Adams were enjoying a fine Sunday morning. Suddenly they noticed a puff of smoke coming from an old volcano 30 miles away. Within seconds the world around them seemed to explode. The earth shook, and black dust blocked the sun. Mount St. Helens had erupted.

That blast from Mount St. Helens was more powerful than a bomb. It blew away the top of the mountain and knocked down trees for miles around. It sent a river of mud crashing into bridges and homes. Falling ash covered farms and cities and was deposited in 11 states. Worst of all, Mount St. Helens was a killer. Dozens of people were dead or missing. The eruption lasted nine hours, but the change in the surrounding landscape was instantaneous.

The mountain had tried to sound a warning. Two months earlier, it had erupted for the first time since 1857. At that time, steam and ash were spewed into the air without injuring anyone. Still, even experts didn't take the volcano seriously.

No one made that mistake after the catastrophe on May 18. Scientists kept a watchful eye on the volcano. Weeks of quiet would be followed by more explosions. Now Mount St. Helens is mostly peaceful. Plants and animals have begun slowly to return to this barren place. From 2004 to 2008, small eruptions began sporadically and a new lava dome grew inside the crater. So no one can predict what this sleeping giant will do.

1 _____

2 _____

3 _____

4 _____

5 _____

6 _____

7 _____

8 _____

Bonus Word

sporadically [spə•RAD•i•kə•lee] (adverb)

off and on; with no regular pattern

Find the Word

Write the word that each group of words tells about.

crater	dome	sporadically	catastrophe	summit
barren	spew	landscape	instantaneous	

1 to send out with great force   _____

2 a sudden disaster   _____

3 the highest point; top   _____

4 scenery   _____

5 bare; without life   _____

6 with no regular pattern   _____

7 a rounded top or roof   _____

8 happening immediately   _____

9 a hollow area shaped like a bowl   _____

Word Work

A suffix is added to the end of a word and changes its part of speech. The suffix *ful* can change a noun to an adjective.

power + ful = powerful (full of power)
    n.   adj.

Add the suffix *ful* to each word below. Write the new word on the line and in the phrase.

1 color + ful = _____   a _____ picture

2 help + ful = _____   a _____ map

3 success + ful = _____   a _____ plan

4 pain + ful = _____   a _____ burn

REVIEW

Read each clue. Then solve the puzzle.

Across

1 the customs of a people
4 happening immediately
8 to exist
10 passed down from one generation to the next
12 the highest point
14 with no regular pattern
15 deer that live in arctic areas
16 something that is a source of wealth
17 a bony growth on the head of an animal

Down

2 land that is viewed as scenery
3 bare; without life
5 tiring
6 a rounded roof
7 a sudden and widespread disaster
8 to gush
9 the use of scientific knowledge in an industry
11 a hollow area shaped like a bowl
13 a thick layer of fat

The Treasures of Lascaux

Study each word and its meaning.

apply (verb) to spread; to put on

applies, applied, applying
Be sure to *apply* sunblock while you are at the beach.

cavern (noun) a very large cave

caverns
Carlsbad *Cavern* in New Mexico is the largest cave in the United States.

ensure (verb) to make sure or certain

ensures, ensured, ensuring
These new skis will *ensure* a smooth ride down the slope.

estimate (verb) to make a guess

estimates, estimated, estimating
Can you *estimate* how much it will cost to fix my watch?

extraordinary (adjective) very unusual

Shaquille O'Neal was an *extraordinary* basketball player.

hasten (verb) to move or act quickly; to hurry

hastens, hastened, hastening
On April 18, 1775, Paul Revere *hastened* to warn his neighbors that the British were coming.

mold (noun) a fuzzy fungus that forms on damp surfaces

molds
Spots of *mold* began to form on the ceiling after the leak.

pierce (verb) to make a hole through

pierces, pierced, piercing
A piece of glass *pierced* the bicycle tire.

Read each sentence below. Complete it with a word from the box.

extraordinary	applied	cavern	hastened
pierce	estimated	ensure	mold

1 Always fasten your seatbelt to _____ a safe ride.

2 Never explore a _____ without the help of an expert guide.

3 We _____ to mow the lawn before it rained.

4 A green _____ began to grow on the stale bread.

5 The spacecrafts *Voyager I* and *II* have sent back _____ pictures of the planet Jupiter.

6 Dad scraped off the old blue paint and then _____ a new coat of red.

7 Gina's parents refused to allow her to _____ her nose.

8 The police _____ that 50,000 people watched the concert.

Read this story. Then go back and circle the words in the passage that you have been studying and write them on the lines below.

An exciting adventure began one late summer day in 1940. Four boys went for a walk in the French countryside near Lascaux. Suddenly a dog belonging to one of them fell down a small hole. To save the dog, the boys made the hole wider and crawled through. They followed a narrow passageway until they entered a large room.

One of the boys had an oil lamp. He lit it, and they began to explore this shadowy world. What they saw amazed them. Primitive paintings of bulls, horses, deer, bears—even a rhinoceros—filled the walls of the cave.

As news of the discovery spread, scientists hastened to study the prehistoric treasure. They estimated that the animals were drawn some 17,000 years ago. They believed that the artists began by cutting outlines of the animals with stone tools. Then they applied color. They used sticks, their fingers, or bits of animal fur as brushes. Sometimes they also showed an arrow piercing the animal's body.

No one is certain why the artists made these paintings. The cavern was probably a special place. The artists may have believed that their drawings had great magic. Maybe the drawings would ensure that there would be good hunting.

When the cave paintings were first found, they were in nearly perfect shape. By 1963, the bright colors had begun to fade. Green and white mold threatened to ruin the art. Since then the cave has been closed to the public. Many people are working hard to preserve this extraordinary tie to our ancestors of long ago.

1 _____

2 _____

3 _____

4 _____

5 _____

6 _____

7 _____

8 _____

Bonus Word

primitive [PRIM•i•tiv] (adjective)
simple or crude

Find the Word

Write the word that each group of words tells about.

| primitive
extraordinary | estimate
hasten | ensure
apply | cavern
mold | pierce |

1 to move quickly   _____

2 to spread   _____

3 a fuzzy fungus that forms on damp surfaces   _____

4 to make a hole through   _____

5 simple or crude   _____

6 very unusual   _____

7 to make a guess   _____

8 a very large cave   _____

9 to make certain   _____

Word Work

A prefix is added to the beginning of a word and changes its meaning. The prefix *en* means "to cause to be."

en + sure = ensure (to cause to be sure)

Look up each word below in a dictionary. Tell how *cause* is part of its meaning. Be ready to share what you have learned with the rest of the class.

1 endear   _____

2 enliven   _____

3 entangle   _____

4 enclose   _____

Colored Cotton

Study each word and its meaning.

associate (verb) to connect in one's mind

associates, associated, associating
I always *associate* fall with pumpkins and apples.

eliminate (verb) to do away with

eliminates, eliminated, eliminating
The company decided to *eliminate* some computer jobs.

entomologist (noun) a person who studies insects

entomologists
The *entomologist* collected moths from the area.

fabric (noun) a material or cloth

fabrics
Mom bought new *fabric* to make curtains.

manufacturer (noun) a maker of something

manufacturers
The *manufacturer* of the tires issued a recall.

pesticide (noun) a chemical used to kill harmful insects

pesticides
Some *pesticides* have been found to be harmful to humans.

resistant (adjective) able to withstand the effect of something

The tent is *resistant* to water.

utilize (verb) to put to use

utilizes, utilized, utilizing
The workers were able to *utilize* the old barn siding on the house.

Read each sentence below. Complete it with a word from the box.

utilize	manufacturer	associate	resistant
fabric	entomologist	pesticide	eliminated

1 Protestors picketed the _____ of the medicine.

2 I _____ robins and daffodils with springtime.

3 The _____ gave a lecture about the West Nile virus.

4 Will you be able to _____ all the leftover cartons?

5 Most kids get a vaccine to become _____ to chicken pox.

6 The _____ on the couch faded over the years.

7 The volleyball team was _____ from the tournament.

8 The farmer used a new _____ on his apple orchards.

Read this story. Then go back and circle the words in the passage that you have been studying and write them on the lines below.

The cotton in your blue jeans was once white. Putting the blue in jeans requires a lot of colored dye. The dye is deadly to plants. Manufacturers of jeans and other clothes that have been dyed have to find a way to get rid of the dye water after it has been used without harming the environment. But what if cotton came in colors so it didn't have to be dyed?

Sally Fox found a way to solve the problems associated with chemical dyes. Fox knew a lot about fabrics because she had been spinning cotton since she was just 12 years old. She was also an entomologist. Fox worked for a company that tried to control pesticide use. Eventually, she found a job that utilized her knowledge of insects and fibers. She went to work for a plant breeder who was trying to create a cotton plant that was resistant to insects. Fox found a cotton plant that insects didn't like. However, the cotton that it produced was grown with very short fibers that made it weak. Because the fibers were weak, it was hard to spin. So Fox tried planting different kinds of seeds and combining the seeds from the best plants. In time she was growing brown cotton that could be spun by machine. She also grew green cotton.

Sally Fox sold her cotton to mills that made them into jeans and other clothes. Because no dye or bleach was used to make the clothes, they were advertised as "natural cottons." Naturally colored cottons eliminate the need for dyeing and help protect the environment.

1 _____

2 _____

3 _____

4 _____

5 _____

6 _____

7 _____

8 _____

Bonus Word

bleach [BLEECH] (noun)

a substance that makes something white or removes the color from

Find the Word

Write the word that each group of words tells about.

eliminate resistant	bleach fabric	pesticide associate	entomologist manufacturer	utilize

1 a person who studies insects   _____

2 to connect in one's mind   _____

3 able to withstand the effects of   _____

4 a substance that removes color   _____

5 to do away with   _____

6 a maker of something using machinery   _____

7 a material or cloth   _____

8 to put to use   _____

9 a chemical used to kill harmful insects _____

Word Work

A suffix is added to the end of a word and changes its part of speech. The suffix *ation* changes a verb to a noun.

associate + ation = association
v.   n.

Add the suffix *ation* to each word below. Write the new word on the line and in the phrase.

1 create + ation = _____ a new _____

2 civilize + ation = _____ a primitive _____

3 eliminate + ation = _____ an instant _____

4 utilize + ation = _____ a practical _____

Read the meanings. Then find and circle each word in the puzzle.
Look across and down.

```
D F E J A S S O C I A T E J P I E R C E
A K N C U F V L X E R K M O E B Z Q A D
E X T R A O R D I N A R Y A S D X Z B P
B P O S E I G I A S J W E S T I M A T E
H T M F A B R I C U H C I W I C K P Y O
L R O S V X E U B R A V L K C E B S Q U
N E L I M I N A T E S R E S I S T A N T
A F O E S D F R N O T B H U D O E Z Q I
P U G T G Y R B C M E L T I E N J I Y L
P R I M I T I V E P N E V C A V E R N I
L O S O M Q U S C W K A M Z G D Y C O Z
Y Q T L K M A N U F A C T U R E R F H E
G M Z D X H F L D N O H G L W X M P T N
```

Across

- to connect in one's mind
- to make a hole through
- very unusual
- to make a guess
- a material or cloth
- to do away with
- able to withstand the effect of something
- simple or crude
- a very large cave
- a maker of something

Down

- to spread; to put on
- a person who studies insects
- a fuzzy fungus
- to make certain
- to act quickly
- a substance that removes color
- a chemical used to kill harmful insects
- to put to use

Underground Conductor

Study each word and its meaning.

activist (noun) a person who brings about changes for a cause

> *Activists* protested the new cement plant on the river.

bandanna (noun) a large, colorful handkerchief worn around the neck

> *bandannas*
> The cowhand pulled his *bandanna* up over his nose to keep out the dust.

cherished (adjective) holding dear; precious

> We hung the *cherished* decorations on the tree.

covert (adjective) secret

> The detectives put together a *covert* plan to capture the suspects.

defiant (adjective) not listening to authority

> The *defiant* student walked out of the room.

exposure (noun) making known

> The *exposure* of the robbery plot put the community at ease.

fugitive (noun) a person who runs away to escape the law

> *fugitives*
> The TV news showed a picture of the dangerous *fugitive*.

perilous (adjective) dangerous; likely to cause harm

> A raft trip down the Colorado River can be a *perilous* ride.

Read each sentence below. Complete it with a word from the box.

exposure	perilous	covert	activists
bandanna	fugitive	cherished	defiant

1 The _____ toddler stomped his feet.

2 My grandmother gave me her _____ locket.

3 Rewards are often offered for the capture of a _____.

4 The undercover agent risked _____ by being seen by the neighbors.

5 Stacey folded her bright pink _____ and used it as a sling.

6 Some of the _____ were arrested during the protest.

7 The government obtained _____ documents from enemy countries.

8 Racecar driving can be a _____ hobby.

Read this story. Then go back and circle the words in the passage that you have been studying and write them on the lines below.

The hardworking, but defiant, young slave tied some scraps of food, a few coins, and a knife in a bandanna. With these few things, Harriet Tubman planned to escape from her Maryland master. When darkness fell, Harriet dashed across the fields and into the woods. She headed toward Philadelphia, where she would be safe. To get there, Harriet traveled on the Underground Railroad.

It was 1849. In the United States, the South permitted slavery. The Underground Railroad was a covert organization of activists that helped slaves escape to the North. This "railroad" did not have real trains. It did have "stations" and "conductors," though. Stations were places where slaves could rest during their perilous journey, without fear of exposure. Conductors were the people who guided the fugitives along the way.

After facing many difficulties, Harriet finally reached Philadelphia. There, a feeling of exhilaration came over her. "I looked at my hands to see if I was the same person now that I was free," she said. "I felt like I was in heaven."

It was not enough for Harriet to be free. She wanted others to have the same cherished gift. This courageous woman returned to the South 19 times. She rescued over 300 slaves, including her own family. Slave owners were furious. They put up a $40,000 reward for her capture. But their plan failed. Once Harriet proudly boasted, "I never ran my train off the track. I never lost a passenger."

1 _____

2 _____

3 _____

4 _____

5 _____

6 _____

7 _____

8 _____

Bonus Word

exhilaration [ig•zil•uh•REY•shun] (noun)
great cheerfulness

Find the Word

Write the word that each group of words tells about.

fugitive exposure	activist covert	defiant cherished	exhilaration bandanna	perilous

1 dangerous; likely to cause harm _____

2 a person who brings about changes for a cause _____

3 making known _____

4 secret _____

5 holding dear; precious _____

6 a large, colorful handkerchief _____

7 great cheerfulness _____

8 not listening to authority _____

9 a person who runs away to escape the law _____

Word Work

A suffix is added to the end of a word and changes its part of speech. The suffix *ous* means "full of." It can change a noun to an adjective.

courage + ous = courageous (full of courage)
　　 n. 　　　　　　　　　 adj.

Add the suffix *ous* to each word below. Write the new word on the line and in the phrase.

1 joy + ous = _____ a _____ song

2 danger + ous = _____ a _____ road

3 poison + ous = _____ a _____ plant

4 hazard + ous = _____ a _____ job

Fire in the Oil Fields

Study each word and its meaning.

debris (noun) the remains of something broken or destroyed

> After the storm, the streets were littered with *debris*.

fatigued (adjective) tired

> The workers were *fatigued* after picking vegetables all day.

hazardous (adjective) full of danger; risky

> Doctors warn that smoking is *hazardous* to your health.

prevention (noun) something that keeps an event from happening

> *preventions*
> Washing your hands is good *prevention* against spreading germs.

retreat (verb) to move back to a position held before

> *retreats, retreated, retreating*
> The troops packed up their gear and *retreated*.

shock (noun) a sudden and violent blow or event

> *shocks*
> The *shock* of the accident caused whiplash.

snuff (verb) to put out or extinguish

> *snuffs, snuffed, snuffing*
> We *snuffed* out the campfire by pouring water on it.

unique (adjective) very special or unusual; being one of a kind

> The trapdoor spider has a *unique* way of getting food.

Read each sentence below. Complete it with a word from the box.

retreated	hazardous	fatigued	debris
unique	snuff	prevention	shock

1 I think this fruit has a _____ taste.

2 The _____ of the amusement park ride gave me a headache.

3 After their long march, the _____ soldiers soon fell asleep.

4 It is very _____ for children to play with matches.

5 The hunters _____ when they spotted a herd of angry elephants.

6 As soon as the parade was over, street sweepers cleaned up the _____.

7 Mom forgot to _____ out the candle before she left the room.

8 We learned about fire _____ from the firefighters.

Read this story. Then go back and circle the words in the passage that you have been studying and write them on the lines below.

Boom! A violent explosion rocks the oil field. Workers standing nearby are pushed back by the force of the blast. Minutes before, the area around the oil well had been quiet. Now, flames reach a height of 500 feet. The workers retreat from the roaring blowout.

Only a few people in the world can handle an oil well fire. Within hours, these special firefighters reach the oil field. They assess the blazing well carefully.

First the crew clears away the debris from the blast. The men wear special fireproof suits. Even so, hoses spray a steady stream of cool water over the crew as prevention. Without it, the firefighters could not stand the heat of 2,000°F. Everyone works with great care. One mistake could cost a life.

Next the firefighters begin work on the flaming well. They decide to fight fire with fire. The crew places a large explosive charge in a barrel. A crane lowers the barrel into the middle of the fire. The shock of the new explosion draws all the air away from the blaze. Fire needs oxygen to burn. So the oil well fire is snuffed out like a giant candle.

But the job is not over. In fact, the most hazardous part is yet to come. The crew must cap the well by placing a cover over it. This work must be done by hand. The firefighters move slowly. A spark from their tools might set off another blast. Finally, the cap is in place and the fatigued crew can rest. What a unique job they have!

1 _____

2 _____

3 _____

4 _____

5 _____

6 _____

7 _____

8 _____

Bonus Word

assess [ə•SES] (verb)
to evaluate

Find the Word

Write the word that each group of words tells about.

hazardous	unique	assess	debris	retreat
prevention	fatigued	shock	snuff	

1 a sudden and violent blow or event _____

2 tired _____

3 full of danger; risky _____

4 very special or unusual _____

5 to put out or extinguish _____

6 the remains of something broken _____

7 to move back to a position held before _____

8 something that keeps an event from happening _____

9 to evaluate _____

Word Work

Compound words are made by joining two other words.

blow + out = blowout

The word *blowout* describes an explosion at an oil well.

Find two words in the list below that can be joined to make a compound word. Write that compound word on a line below. Do the same for the remaining words. Be ready to discuss your new words.

off	life	shirt	down	sweat	week
touch	end	paper	rip	guard	back

_____   _____

_____   _____

_____   _____

REVIEW

Read each meaning. Write the word in the blanks. Read the words down the boxes.
They are something you might hear shouted after an oil well explosion.

1 ☐ __ __ __ __ __ __ __ __ __
2 __ __ __ __ ☐ __ __ __ __ __
3 __ __ __ __ ☐ __ __
4 __ __ __ __ ☐ __ __ __ __ __ __
5 __ __ ☐ __ __ __ __
6 __ __ __ ☐ __ __ __ __ __
7 __ __ ☐ __ __ __ __ __
8 __ __ ☐ __ __ __ __
9 __ __ ☐ __ __ __ __
10 __ __ ☐ __ __ __ __
11 __ __ ☐ __ __ __ __
12 __ __ ☐ __ __ __ __
13 __ __ ☐ __ __ __ __
14 __ __ ☐ __ __ __ __
15 __ __ __ __ ☐ __ __ __ __ __ __
16 __ __ __ __ ☐ __ __ __
17 __ __ __ ☐ __ __ __ __

Definitions

1 a person who escapes the law
2 holding dear; precious
3 secret
4 something that keeps an event from happening
5 to evaluate
6 a large, colorful handkerchief
7 very tired
8 to put out
9 worthless remains
10 a sudden, violent blow
11 unlike anything else
12 not listening to authority
13 a person who brings about changes for a cause
14 to go back to where you were
15 great cheerfulness
16 very dangerous, risky
17 making known

Bertha von Suttner

Study each word and its meaning.

acclaimed (adjective) celebrated, praised

> Mayor Weston is one of the most *acclaimed* citizens of this town.

aristocratic (adjective) noble; relating to wealthy society

> Kings and queens are born to *aristocratic* families.

correspond (verb) to exchange letters with someone

> *corresponds, corresponded, corresponding*
> Jazmine and her friends *correspond* with text messages.

explosive (noun) a substance that can blow up

> *explosives*
> The contractor used *explosives* to bring down the old building.

lecture (verb) to give an informational speech

> *lectures, lectured, lecturing*
> The professor *lectured* about the Vietnam War era.

promote (verb) to help the growth or progress of

> *promotes, promoted, promoting*
> The author went on book signings to *promote* his new book.

recruit (verb) to get a person to join

> *recruits, recruited, recruiting*
> The coach *recruited* girls to play on the soccer team.

vigorous (adjective) done with great energy

> Mom took a *vigorous* swim in the cold ocean.

Read each sentence below. Complete it with a word from the box.

explosives	corresponds	acclaimed	promote
lectured	recruit	aristocratic	vigorous

1 The agent sent the band out to _____ the new album.

2 Mom _____ me about the importance of doing my homework.

3 My teacher _____ with parents once a month.

4 The heiress was disowned by her _____ family.

5 Dynamite and TNT are powerful _____.

6 We took a _____ two-mile walk.

7 The marine visited the high school to _____ people for the service.

8 The statue showed the town's _____ founder.

Read this story. Then go back and circle the words in the passage that you have been studying and write them on the lines below.

Chances are you've never heard of Bertha von Suttner. Not many people have. But she was a very important figure in the history of pacifism, the struggle to stop war and keep peace. Von Suttner also helped bring about one of the most acclaimed prizes in the world, the Nobel Peace Prize.

Bertha von Suttner was born in 1843, the product of an aristocratic family. As she grew up, she realized that the world was not a perfect place. Many wars were being fought, and people were dying senselessly. Von Suttner wanted to stop all that. She had a vigorous opposition to military positions. She studied the current wars and fighting. With all that she learned, she wrote a novel called *Lay Down Your Arms*. Many people read von Suttner's novel.

But von Suttner didn't stop there. She wrote about why peace was better than war. She corresponded with people all over the world to promote peace projects. She traveled far and wide to recruit people and lectured others to "lay down their arms." She became famous for her position against war.

In her travels, von Suttner met many important people. One of the first of those people was Alfred Nobel. Nobel was a chemist who was developing explosives for war and for railroads. He, too, was a pacifist, but a different sort of pacifist. He wanted to scare people out of war and into peace by making the most horrible, destructive weapon anyone could imagine. When people saw how awful the weapon was, they would be too scared to fight. Wars would come to an end.

Though they had their differences, von Suttner and Nobel became lifelong friends. Nobel came to many of von Suttner's peace meetings, and he gave some of his sizable wealth to her peace organizations. Eventually, von Suttner convinced Nobel to establish a fund for a yearly peace prize. The prize was first awarded in 1901. Von Suttner herself won the Nobel Peace Prize in 1905.

1 _____

2 _____

3 _____

4 _____

5 _____

6 _____

7 _____

8 _____

Bonus Word

pacifist [PAS•ə•fist] (noun)
a person who is against war

Find the Word

Write the word that each group of words tells about.

recruit	promote	vigorous	aristocratic	acclaimed
pacifist	explosive	lecture	correspond	

1 to help the growth or progress of   _____

2 to give an informational speech   _____

3 to exchange letters with someone   _____

4 done with great energy   _____

5 a substance that can blow up   _____

6 to get a person to join   _____

7 noble; relating to wealthy society   _____

8 a person who is against war   _____

9 celebrated, praised   _____

Word Work

Homophones are words that sound alike but are spelled differently. They also have different meanings.

one single   **won** to be victorious

Look up these pairs of homophones in the dictionary. Write their meanings on the lines below and be ready to use them in a sentence.

heard _____

herd _____

peace _____

piece _____

The Unfinished Zebra

Study each word and its meaning.

converge (verb) to move towards one point

converges, converged, converging
All of the seventh-grade classes *converged* in the cafeteria.

existence (noun) the state of being

My aunt believes in the *existence* of ghosts.

exterminate (verb) to get rid of by destroying completely

exterminates, exterminated, exterminating
The pest company *exterminated* the termites in our house.

irreversible (adverb) unable to be changed or reversed

The king's decree was *irreversible*.

resemble (verb) to be like; to look like

resembles, resembled, resembling
After the rain, our street *resembled* a large pond.

slaughter (verb) to kill in large numbers

slaughters, slaughtered, slaughtering
Many animals are *slaughtered* for their hides.

stampede (verb) to flee wildly; to rush away suddenly in a group

stampedes, stampeded, stampeding
A clap of thunder caused the horses to *stampede*.

tragic (adjective) extremely sad or fatal

The news program showed a *tragic* story about a homeless woman.

Read each sentence below. Complete it with a word from the box.

irreversible	**tragic**	**slaughtered**	**stampeded**
resemble	**converge**	**existence**	**exterminate**

1 The town put up a monument for the victims of the _____ fire.

2 We will have to _____ the rodents who have infested the barn.

3 Will all the performers please _____ backstage?

4 Weren't you afraid when the elephants _____ toward the camp?

5 The effects of some diseases are _____.

6 This book is about wolves' _____ in Yellowstone National Park.

7 My friends say that I _____ my sister.

8 Hunters once _____ buffaloes until they almost disappeared.

Read this story. Then go back and circle the words in the passage that you have been studying and write them on the lines below.

Someone once said that the quagga looked like an unfinished zebra. This animal was about the size of a small horse. It had a light brown body with stripes on only the head, neck, and front part. A dark brown line ran down the middle of its back. Its legs were white with black hoofs. Its ears and tail resembled those of a donkey. The name quagga (KWAG•uh) came from the loud barking sound it made.

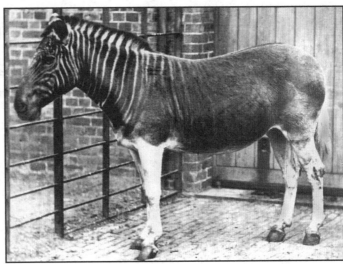

The story of the quagga is a tragic one. Immense herds of these wild animals were native to the grasslands of South Africa, where they roamed freely. When they stampeded, the noise was like a great storm.

As settlers from Europe converged on Africa, the quagga's existence was irreversibly changed. The settlers didn't like the taste of quagga meat, but their workers did. The settlers slaughtered the animals by the thousands to feed the workers.

Quaggas were easy to tame. It would have been simple to raise them the way cattle are raised. But no one thought to do that. People kept on hunting and killing the quagga. They were exterminated in the wild in the 1870s. By 1873, only one quagga survived. It died in captivity in 1883.

1 _____

2 _____

3 _____

4 _____

5 _____

6 _____

7 _____

8 _____

Bonus Word

captivity [kap•TIV•i•tee] (noun)
under someone's control

Find the Word

Write the word that each group of words tells about.

tragic	captivity	converge	irreversible	resemble
existence	slaughter	stampede	exterminate	

1 under someone's control   _____

2 extremely sad or fatal   _____

3 the state of being   _____

4 to kill in large numbers   _____

5 unable to be changed   _____

6 to flee wildly   _____

7 to move towards one point   _____

8 to look like   _____

9 to get rid of by destroying completely   _____

Word Work

A prefix is added to the beginning of a word and changes its meaning. The prefix *un* can mean "not."

un + finished = unfinished (not finished)

Add the prefix *un* to each word below. Write the new word on the line and in the phrase.

1 un + happy = _____   an _____ clown

2 un + expected = _____   an _____ guest

3 un + locked = _____   an _____ door

4 un + prepared = _____   an _____ student

Read each clue. Then solve the puzzle.

Across

1 to kill in large numbers
3 to get rid of by destroying completely
6 extremely sad or fatal
8 celebrated
10 to look like
11 under someone's control
13 to exchange letters with someone
14 done with great energy
15 to get a person to join
16 unable to be changed

Down

1 to flee wildly
2 a substance that can blow up
4 the state of being
5 a person who is against war
7 relating to wealthy society
9 to give an informational speech
11 to move towards one point
12 to help the growth of something

The Great Wall of China

Study each word and its meaning.

continuous (adjective) keeping on without stopping

Some parts of the world have weeks of *continuous* sunshine.

emperor (noun) the male ruler of an empire

emperors
Akihito became *emperor* of Japan in 1989.

plague (verb) to trouble or torment

plagues, plagued, plaguing
The pain in my ankle *plagued* me all day.

satellite (noun) an object launched into orbit to study Earth

satellites
Many television channels are transmitted by *satellite*.

sentry (noun) a soldier standing guard

sentries
The *sentry* would not allow me to enter without a password.

structure (noun) something that has been built; a building

structures
A vacant *structure* across the street caught fire.

transmit (verb) to send

transmits, transmitted, transmitting
My dad used the computer to *transmit* information to his boss.

welfare (noun) the health and happiness of a group

This group is concerned about the *welfare* of orphans.

Read each sentence below. Complete it with a word from the box.

plagued	transmitted	sentries	welfare
satellites	continuous	emperor	structure

1 Two _____ stood outside the palace gate.

2 NASA has many _____ orbiting Earth.

3 I saw a movie about Pu Yi, the last _____ of China.

4 Dad built a small _____ to store the lawn equipment.

5 I am worried about my grandmother's _____ since she has been sick.

6 I was _____ with worries about the big math test.

7 At one time, messages were _____ by telegraph.

8 The telethon ran for twenty-four _____ hours.

Read this story. Then go back and circle the words in the passage that you have been studying and write them on the lines below.

Over 2,200 years ago, the emperor of China was plagued with concern about attacks by his enemies. To defend his country, he decided to build a wall along its northern border.

The emperor placed one of his generals in charge of more than one million workers. For seven years these people labored through the heat of summer and the cold of winter. They dug deep ditches for the base of the wall. They made bricks from clay and piled them one on top of another. The general did not care about the welfare of the workers. Thousands of them perished, and their bodies were often buried inside the wall. Finally, the main part of the wall was completed. Later rulers added to it. The last part was built just 350 years ago.

The Great Wall of China was not a single, continuous structure. It stretched like a giant brick snake for more than 1,500 miles. The wall was about 15 to 30 feet wide at the base and 24 feet tall. Its top was wide enough for eight soldiers to march side by side. Every few hundred yards along the wall there were 40-foot-high watchtowers. Here sentries patrolled night and day, looking carefully for signs of trouble.

Parts of the huge wall are still standing today and are popular tourist destinations. The wall is also discernible in pictures transmitted back by satellites in space.

1 _____

2 _____

3 _____

4 _____

5 _____

6 _____

7 _____

8 _____

Bonus Word

discernible [di•SURN•ə•bəl] (adjective)
able to be comprehended

Find the Word

Write the word that each group of words tells about.

sentry	discernible	welfare	emperor	transmit
plague	continuous	satellite	structure	

1 to trouble or torment   _____

2 keeping on without stopping   _____

3 a soldier standing guard   _____

4 an object launched into orbit to study Earth   _____

5 to send   _____

6 able to be comprehended   _____

7 a male ruler of an empire   _____

8 something that has been built   _____

9 the health and happiness of a group   _____

Word Work

Synonyms are words that mean the same, or almost the same, thing.

perish • die   **complete • finish**

Find a synonym for each of the following words. Check a dictionary for help. Write the synonyms on the lines below. Be ready to use them in a sentence.

1 odor   _____   4 purchase   _____

2 cautious   _____   5 respond   _____

3 applaud   _____   6 accurate   _____

Earth and the Moon

Study each word and its meaning.

diminish (verb) to make smaller or less

diminishes, diminished, diminishing
The amount of bread at the bakery was greatly *diminished* by the end of the day.

illuminate (verb) to light up

illuminates, illuminated, illuminating
The lamp in the corner *illuminates* the entire room.

partial (adjective) not complete, some of

I could only eat a *partial* sandwich for lunch.

phase (noun) a step in a process

phases
We are in the first *phase* of remodeling the house.

prominent (adjective) most easily seen

The mayor was given a *prominent* position at the banquet.

sliver (noun) a small, narrow piece of something

slivers
Only a *sliver* of the sun shone through the clouds.

solitary (adjective) by itself, alone

A *solitary* tree stood in the field.

wane (verb) to slowly get smaller in size or power

wanes, waned, waning
As evening came, the light began to *wane*.

Read each sentence below. Complete it with a word from the box.

solitary	prominent	illuminate	wane
diminished	sliver	phase	partial

1 Jeremy finished the final _____ of his history project.

2 A _____ cloud floated in the blue sky.

3 Mr. Smith's influence in the company _____ as he grew older.

4 Use a flashlight to _____ this dark corner.

5 On Friday, we only have a _____ day of school.

6 Kurt's excitement over being in the play began to _____.

7 There is only a _____ of pie left in the pan.

8 Red is the _____ color in this painting.

Read this story. Then go back and circle the words in the passage that you have been studying and write them on the lines below.

Every planet in the solar system, except for Mercury and Venus, has at least one moon. A moon is a small object that revolves around a planet. Some planets have many moons. Earth has only one. The moon is Earth's solitary natural satellite. It is usually the most prominent feature in the night sky.

Although the moon seems to shine, it does not actually produce its own light. It reflects light from the sun. This light illuminates half the moon at all times. However, we usually only see a partial amount of the illuminated half of the moon.

As the moon orbits Earth, its position relative to Earth and the sun changes. This causes the moon's appearance to change. The moon has eight basic phases. It changes phases every three to four days, and it moves through all its phases in about 29 days. This period of time is called a lunar cycle. At the end of the lunar cycle, the moon looks the same as it did at the beginning. Then the process starts again.

During the waxing phase, the illuminated part of the moon appears to become larger. We say the moon is waning when the illuminated part appears to diminish. A crescent moon looks like a small sliver of light because most of the lighted part of the moon faces away from Earth. We see a full moon when the entire illuminated side of the moon faces us. When the entire illuminated side faces away, we cannot see the moon at all. This phase is called new moon.

1 _____

2 _____

3 _____

4 _____

5 _____

6 _____

7 _____

8 _____

Bonus Word

lunar [LOO•ner] (adjective)
related to the moon

Find the Word

Write the word that each group of words tells about.

prominent	lunar	solitary	wane	illuminate
diminish	sliver	partial	phase	

1 to light up _____

2 to make smaller or less _____

3 related to the moon _____

4 to slowly get smaller in size or power _____

5 a step in a process _____

6 by itself _____

7 most easily seen _____

8 a small, narrow piece of something _____

9 not complete _____

Word Work

Root words are used to build other words. The root word *cycl* comes from a Greek word that means "circle" or "wheel." You can find this root word in a number of English words.

cycle a set of events that repeats

Look up each word below in a dictionary. Tell how "circle" or "wheel" is part of its meaning. Be ready to share what you have learned with the rest of the class.

1 cyclone _____

2 motorcycle _____

3 recycle _____

4 cyclist _____

Read each meaning. Write the word in the blanks. Read the words down the boxes.
They name a man whose teachings became one of China's major religions.

1 ☐ __ __ __ __

2 __ __ __ __ ☐ __ __

3 __ ☐ __ __ __ __ __

4 __ __ __ __ ☐

5 __ __ ☐ __ __ __ __ __ __

6 __ __ ☐ __ __ __ __

7 __ ☐ __ __ __ __ __

8 __ __ __ ☐ __ __

9 __ __ __ __ __ __ ☐ __

10 __ __ ☐ __ __ __

11 __ __ ☐ __ __ __

12 __ __ ☐ __ __

13 __ __ __ ☐ __ __ __ __ __ __

14 __ __ __ ☐ __ __ __

15 __ __ __ ☐ __ __ __ __

16 ☐ __ __ __ __ __ __ __

Definitions

1 to slowly get smaller in size
2 not complete
3 a small, narrow piece of something
4 a step in a process
5 keeping on without stopping
6 to trouble or torment
7 to make smaller or less
8 a building
9 the male ruler of an empire
10 a guard
11 the health and happiness of a group
12 related to the moon
13 able to be comprehended
14 alone
15 to light up
16 an object launched into orbit to study Earth

Circle the correct answer.

1. Flower is to daisy as **fabric** is to _____.
   A victim
   B landscape
   C velvet
   D quilt

2. Glove is to hand as **bandanna** is to _____.
   A feet
   B finger
   C blubber
   D head

3. Tame is to wild as **unique** is to _____.
   A common
   B extraordinary
   C propel
   D ugly

4. Chef is to cook as **sentry** is to _____.
   A read
   B stand
   C guard
   D teach

5. Descend is to down as **summit** is to _____.
   A bottom
   B top
   C round
   D dome

6. What is something that is usually **hazardous?**
   A a coat
   B a door
   C a telephone
   D a fire

7. What would probably cause a lot of **debris?**
   A a football game
   B a hurricane
   C a street cleaner
   D a garden hose

8. What does a **pacifist** want?
   A war
   B peace
   C money
   D food

9. Where might you find **mold?**
   A in your math book
   B on your computer screen
   C in your refrigerator
   D on your shirt sleeve

10. Which of the following is a **structure?**
    A a crater
    B a shed
    C a satellite
    D a rooster

POSTTEST

Complete each sentence with a word from the box.

traditional	fatigued	correspond	barren	utilized	promote
instantaneously	vigorous	estimated	resemble	defiant	
eliminated	solitary	cherished	phase	plagued	

1 I had a _____ workout at hockey practice.

2 The college _____ its art program.

3 The next _____ of the project is to paint each piece of wood.

4 We had a _____ German meal at the restaurant.

5 The wildfire left the landscape _____.

6 A digital camera shows the pictures _____.

7 We _____ that it took 20 hours to complete the project.

8 The kindergarten teacher _____ every inch of space in her classroom.

9 Maddy took her _____ teddy bear to camp with her.

10 We added fertilizer to the lawn to help _____ the grass's growth.

11 My cousins and I _____ at least once a month.

12 The _____ protestor ended up in jail.

13 Some people say that I _____ my grandfather.

14 Mom was _____ from pulling weeds all day.

15 Anton was _____ with fear of giving his speech.

16 Only a _____ tree was left in the tornado's path.

access: *(noun)* permission to use something

acclaimed: *(adjective)* celebrated; praised

accomplish: *(verb)* to carry out; to complete

activist: *(noun)* a person who brings about changes for a cause

alliance: *(noun)* an agreement between two or more countries

antler: *(noun)* a bony growth on the head of an animal, such as a deer

apply: *(verb)* to spread; to put on

archaeologist: *(noun)* a person who studies how people lived in the past

aristocratic: *(adjective)* noble; relating to wealthy society

artery: *(noun)* part of the body that carries blood away from the heart

assemble: *(verb)* to put together

assess: *(verb)* to evaluate

associate: *(verb)* to connect in one's mind

astronomer: *(noun)* a person who studies objects in space

atmosphere: *(noun)* the air that surrounds Earth

attraction: *(noun)* something that draws people's attention

automatic: *(adjective)* operating by itself

bandanna: *(noun)* a large, colorful handkerchief worn around the neck

barren: *(adjective)* bare; without life

barrier: *(noun)* something that blocks movement

bestow: *(verb)* to present as a gift

betray: *(verb)* to hand over to an enemy; to not be loyal to

bleach: *(noun)* a substance that makes something white or removes the color from

blubber: *(noun)* a thick layer of fat under the skin of sea animals

captivity: *(noun)* under someone's control

caribou: *(noun)* deer that live in arctic areas

catastrophe: *(noun)* a sudden and widespread disaster

cavern: *(noun)* a very large cave

centennial: *(noun)* a 100th anniversary

chariot: *(noun)* a two-wheeled cart pulled by horses

cherished: *(adjective)* holding dear; precious

collapse: *(verb)* to cave in; to fall apart

communicate: *(verb)* to pass information so that it is received and understood

component: *(noun)* a part of something; an ingredient

confident: *(adjective)* very sure; certain

continuous: *(adjective)* keeping on without stopping

contract: *(verb)* to draw all parts together

converge: *(verb)* to move towards one point

converse: *(verb)* to talk with someone

cooperate: *(verb)* to work together

correspond: *(verb)* to exchange letters with someone

covert: *(adjective)* secret

crater: *(noun)* a hollow area shaped like a bowl

cruelty: *(noun)* unkind, painful words or actions

culture: *(noun)* the customs or ways of living of a people

debris: *(noun)* the remains of something broken or destroyed

deduct: *(verb)* to take away from an account

defiant: *(adjective)* not listening to authority

deposit: *(verb)* to put money into an account

diary: *(noun)* a daily record of a person's acts and thoughts

digest: *(verb)* to change food so it can be used by the body

diminish: *(verb)* to make smaller or less

discernible: *(adjective)* able to be comprehended

dispense: *(verb)* to give out

diversify: *(verb)* to give a variety to; vary

dome: *(noun)* a rounded top or roof like a half sphere

economy: *(noun)* management of money and goods

eliminate: *(verb)* to do away with

emperor: *(noun)* the male ruler of an empire

endanger: *(verb)* to threaten or expose to harm

ensure: *(verb)* to make sure or certain

entertain: *(verb)* to hold the attention of; to amuse

entomologist: *(noun)* a person who studies insects

eradicate: *(verb)* to get rid of completely

esteem: *(noun)* good opinion; great respect

estimate: *(verb)* to make a guess

excavation: *(noun)* the act of digging something out

exhilaration: *(noun)* great cheerfulness

existence: *(noun)* the state of being

expand: *(verb)* to become larger; to grow in size

expel: *(verb)* to force out or discharge

explosive: *(noun)* a substance that can blow up

exposure: *(noun)* making known

exterminate: *(verb)* to get rid of by destroying completely

extraordinary: *(adjective)* very unusual

extreme: *(adjective)* very great in measure

fabric: *(noun)* a material or cloth

fatigued: *(adjective)* tired

federal: *(adjective)* relating to the central government of a country

forbid: *(verb)* to not allow; to order not to do

fugitive: *(noun)* a person who runs away to escape the law

function: *(noun)* the specific purpose for something

gesture: *(noun)* a motion of the hands, arms, or body while speaking or in place of speech

gorilla: *(noun)* a large African ape with a heavy body and dark hair

grueling: *(adjective)* tiring; exhausting

guarantee: *(verb)* to promise; to make certain

habitat: *(noun)* a place where a plant or animal naturally lives

hasten: *(verb)* to move or act quickly; to hurry

hatred: *(noun)* a very strong dislike

hazardous: *(adjective)* full of danger; risky

holocaust: *(noun)* total destruction and great loss of life

illuminate: *(verb)* to light up

inflate: *(verb)* to fill with air

GLOSSARY

inhale: *(verb)* to breathe in

install: *(verb)* to put in a position for use

instantaneous: *(adjective)* happening immediately

insulate: *(verb)* to cover with a material that prevents heat from escaping

internal: *(adjective)* located inside or within; inner

irreversible: *(adverb)* unable to be changed or reversed

jewelry: *(noun)* objects, such as rings and necklaces, worn on the body

landscape: *(noun)* land that is viewed as scenery

larva: *(noun)* the wormlike form of a newly hatched insect

lecture: *(verb)* to give an informational speech

lunar: *(adjective)* related to the moon

manufacturer: *(noun)* a maker of something

massive: *(adjective)* very large and heavy

memory: *(noun)* honor and respect for someone in the past

mold: *(noun)* a fuzzy fungus that forms on damp surfaces

mummy: *(noun)* a body that has been preserved after death

nutrient: *(noun)* something that helps supply what is needed for life and health

occasionally: *(adverb)* happening only from time to time

occupy: *(verb)* to take over and control something

pacifist: *(noun)* a person who is against war

partial: *(adjective)* not complete, some of

payment: *(noun)* money given in exchange for goods or services

penetrate: *(verb)* to see or pass through

perilous: *(adjective)* dangerous; likely to cause harm

personification: *(noun)* the representation of an idea or thing as a person

pesticide: *(noun)* a chemical used to kill harmful insects

pharaoh: *(noun)* the title of a ruler of ancient Egypt

phase: *(noun)* a step in a process

pierce: *(verb)* to make a hole through

plague: *(verb)* to trouble or torment

pollute: *(verb)* to make the environment dirty or impure

prevention: *(noun)* something that keeps an event from happening

primitive: *(adjective)* simple or crude

probable: *(adjective)* most likely

profitable: *(adjective)* making money

prominent: *(adjective)* most easily seen

promote: *(verb)* to help the growth or progress of

provision: *(noun)* a part of an agreement

publish: *(verb)* to print and offer for sale

ravaged: *(adjective)* completely destroyed

recover: *(verb)* to get back again

recruit: *(verb)* to get a person to join

reflect: *(verb)* to send back light rays from a surface

repetition: *(noun)* saying or doing something again and again

resemble: *(verb)* to be like; to look like

resistant: *(adjective)* able to withstand the effect of something

resource: *(noun)* something that is a source of wealth

retain: *(verb)* to keep; to hold in

retreat: *(verb)* to move back to a position held before

sacred: *(adjective)* holy

satellite: *(noun)* an object launched into orbit to study Earth

scrutinize: *(verb)* to look at carefully

sculptor: *(noun)* a person who shapes clay or carves in wood, stone, or some other material

selective: *(adjective)* choosy or picky

sentry: *(noun)* a soldier standing guard

shock: *(noun)* a sudden and violent blow or event

slaughter: *(verb)* to kill in large numbers

sliver: *(noun)* a small, narrow piece of something

snout: *(noun)* the long front part of the head of an animal

snuff: *(verb)* to put out or extinguish

solitary: *(adjective)* by itself, alone

species: *(noun)* a group of similar plants or animals

spectacular: *(adjective)* unusual and impressive

speculate: *(verb)* to come up with an idea that is mostly based on theory

spew: *(verb)* to gush or send out with force

sporadically: *(adverb)* off and on; with no regular pattern

stampede: *(verb)* to flee wildly; to rush away suddenly in a group

structure: *(noun)* something that has been built; a building

subsist: *(verb)* to exist

summit: *(noun)* the highest point; top

supreme: *(adjective)* highest in degree

technology: *(noun)* the use of scientific knowledge in an industry

tomb: *(noun)* a place to hold a dead body

traditional: *(adjective)* passed down from one generation to the next

tragic: *(adjective)* extremely sad or fatal

transaction: *(noun)* a business dealing

transmit: *(verb)* to send

typically: *(adverb)* usually, most often

tyranny: *(noun)* the cruel use of power

unique: *(adjective)* very special or unusual; being one of a kind

unveil: *(verb)* to disclose or bring into view

usurp: *(verb)* to take by force, usually without rights

utilize: *(verb)* to put to use

velocity: *(noun)* speed

vigorous: *(adjective)* done with great energy

wane: *(verb)* to slowly get smaller in size or power

welfare: *(noun)* the health and happiness of a group